Partner
BETRAYAL TRAUMA
The Workbook

DOUGLAS WEISS, PH.D.

Table of Contents

Printed in the United States of America
ISBN# 978-1-881292-41-8

Requests for information:

Discovery Press
heart2heart@xc.org
719-278-3708

Cover and Interior Design by Janelle Evangelides

Introduction

Your betrayal is real. The pain, grief, and devastation that has impacted your whole being as well as all areas of your life from your partner's betrayal is real. Sadly, you're not alone. Millions of women have been betrayed by their husbands and significant others sexually and in so many other ways.

This workbook honors your journey, validates your pain and gives you a proven path to empower yourself back to the amazing woman you were before the trauma. You're being guided by someone who has helped heal thousands of betrayed women for more than thirty years.

The strengthening and insights you will gain can give you hope to live an amazing life regardless of your husband's or significant other's past, present or future choices. Your courage to remove the shrapnel from your heart caused by the grenade of his betrayal is inspiring. In your hands you hold a resource that will allow you to take one step at a time to heal, process, and help you become stronger than you thought possible.

Our hope and prayer as you go through this workbook by yourself, with a friend or in a group is that you'll become the best you. Our desire for you is that this journey will not only be worth pursuing but that you will use your strength to eventually encourage others that have been betrayed.

For more information or to place orders, contact us at:
Heart to Heart Counseling Center
719-278-3708
www.drdougweiss.com
heart2heart@xc.org

In the book *Partner Betrayal Trauma*, I start with the subject of trust. I do this because that's where the journey with your husband or significant other began.

When you began to date him, he was charming, caring and thoughtful. Whatever else he did during the course of dating he got you to trust him or the version of him he was selling. He got you to give your whole heart to him. He was your prince charming, the one you could commit everything to and the one who would protect you. You walked down the aisle of marriage and before God, family, and friends committed to you and were all in.

You have lived life together, and maybe have even had children or grandchildren. You have a history prior to the betrayal. You have a story. You were a good woman, friend, lover, caretaker, manager and nurse.

This part of the story is important to acknowledge to yourself. Your undying trust and giving all of your complete self is why you have so much pain. His choice to betray you, and sometimes repeatedly betray you, have been crushing blows for you to absorb.

On the lines below, write and give examples of how prior to your knowledge of his betrayal, you trusted (sometimes blindly) him in these areas of your life.

In my emotions I trusted him:

Socially I trusted him:

Spiritually I trusted him:

Sexually I trusted him:

Financially I trusted him:

I trusted him with our neighbors:

I trusted him with his time:

I trusted his words:

I trusted him with things around the house:

I trusted him with my secrets:

I trusted him with my dreams:

I trusted him with my body:

I trusted him with the children:

I trusted him with holidays:

I trusted him with my heart:

As you look over your notes, what did you learn about yourself?

As you look at your previous work, what have you learned about him?

You were an "all in" woman. Write about what being "all in" meant.

For some women the trust started to erode before the knowledge of his betrayal became known. If that is your story, write about what areas of life your trust was weakening prior to the knowledge of his betrayal and why it was weakening.

Area 1 was

____

Area 2 was

____

Area 3 was

____

Area 4 was

____

Area 5 was ________________

As you look at these areas of mistrust, what did you learn about:

Yourself:

Him:

When you look at the previous areas of this trust, what are the onesa that are strongest for you currently?

1. ______
2. ______
3. ______
4. ______
5. ______

What are you looking for from him to re-establish trust?

What may be required of you to move forward in trust?

____

____

____

____

____

____

____

____

Trust is a very big issue. You extended the gift of trust so freely to your husband or significant other. You had nothing to do with his choice to damage this gift. Trust can be rebuilt over time. For now, just know that you being "all in" is why the pain is so real and so multi-faceted.

As you walk through the book, this workbook, and interact with other amazing women, my desire is that your strength and hope increases so you can reclaim yourself and your life.

My insights from this section are:

1. ____
2. ____
3. ____
4. ____
5. ____

I decide to share this work with ________________________ *on* ____/____/____.

Partners who have been betrayed by their husbands or significant others might have little to major previous trauma or neglect, no previous trauma, or repressed trauma. In the following pages we will journey through the potential betrayals including abuse and/or neglect that your soul, body or sexuality has experienced prior to being betrayed in your relationship.

Your current portrait is unique to you. Your trauma history is also unique to you. This history can help you identify issues that arise from being re-injured or re-bruised because of the current trauma. As some women heal, they also gain insight or patterns that contribute to helping them heal.

Let's begin this journey where all our journeys begin—in our family. Before we take one step on this journey let's establish the following truths:

1. NO betrayal, trauma, or neglect you've experienced from anyone is your fault.
2. Your husband's or partner's choice to betray you has nothing to do with you.
3. Your past trauma history has no bearing on his choice to betray you.

Now, let's review positive areas of trauma you may have experienced. Be completely honest. Many women hide their past trauma for many reasons. I can't tell you the countless times a partner of betrayal trauma has told me, "Dr. Weiss, you're the first person I've ever told."

If you're one of these women, please break the promise within your heart to "never to tell anyone." We cannot heal or even understand ourselves if we can't be honest about our histories. Let's move on to our family.

My Dad and Addictions:

Alcohol ____Y ____N
Drugs ____Y ____N
Work ____Y ____N
Sex ____Y ____N
Porn ____Y ____N
Food ____Y ____N
Other ____Y ____N

My Mom and Addictions:

Alcohol ____Y ____N
Drugs ____Y ____N
Work ____Y ____N
Sex ____Y ____N
Porn ____Y ____N
Food ____Y ____N
Other ____Y ____N

My Dad and Abuse:

Physical Abuse	____Y ____N
Emotional Abuse	____Y ____N
Sexual Abuse	____Y ____N
Financial Abuse	____Y ____N
Spiritual Abuse	____Y ____N

My Mom and Abuse:

Physical Abuse	____Y ____N
Emotional Abuse	____Y ____N
Sexual Abuse	____Y ____N
Financial Abuse	____Y ____N
Spiritual Abuse	____Y ____N

My Dad and Neglect:

Physical	____Y ____N
Emotional	____Y ____N
Sexual	____Y ____N
Financial	____Y ____N
Spiritual	____Y ____N
Moral	____Y ____N

My Mom and Neglect:

Physical	____Y ____N
Emotional	____Y ____N
Sexual	____Y ____N
Financial	____Y ____N
Spiritual	____Y ____N
Moral	____Y ____N

I have experienced physical trauma like accidents or surgeries. List below.

1.____

2.____

3.____

4.____

5.____

I have had unwanted or forced sexual encounters? If yes, list areas below (i.e., ages 5-7, 15)

I believe as an adult I have been raped. (If so, at what age?)

1.

2.

3.

4.

I have experienced abortions. If yes, write ages below.

I have experienced seeing someone die.

I have experienced illness(es) in my life. (if yes, put disease and age)

1.____________________________________

2.____________________________________

3.____________________________________

4.____________________________________

I have experienced a crime being perpetrated against me. (i.e., robbed)
If yes, put year and incident.

1.____________________________________

2.____________________________________

3.____________________________________

4.____________________________________

In my previous romantic relationships or marriages, I have experienced my significant other romantically/sexually cheat on me. If yes, write age below.

1.________________________ 6.________________________

2.________________________ 7.________________________

3.________________________ 8.________________________

4.________________________ 9.________________________

5.________________________ 10.________________________

I have had girlfriends who cheated with my romantic interest or husband(s).

If yes, write name and year below.

1.______________________________

2.______________________________

3.______________________________

4.______________________________

5.______________________________

In my previous/current marriage or romantic relationships I have experienced Intimacy Anorexia? (intimacyanorexia.com). If so, write name of person and year below

1.______________________________

2.______________________________

3.______________________________

4.______________________________

5.______________________________

I have had financial trauma happen. If yes, list year and circumstance(s):

1.______________________________

2.______________________________

3.______________________________

4.______________________________

5.______________________________

If you believe you have experienced other traumas or *Betrayal Trauma* that have not been addressed here, please list below.

1______________________________

2______________________________

3______________________________

4______________________________

5______________________________

6______________________________

You have walked through your potential trauma history. Were there any themes or patterns you see in your life as it relates to trauma? If so, list here:

As you look over the previous pages I want you to write out couple of narratives as it relates to your unique trauma journey up to the present betrayal.

I have shared my trauma narrative with ________________ on ____/_____/___.

Understanding and working through betrayal for some women is a process. Sadly, while the process of him betraying you has taken place over the course of months or years without your conscious knowledge, it is still going on in reality.

In counseling with thousands of betrayed women for more than thirty years, I've been in the room as they hear for the first time the actual timeline of his betrayals. He discloses his pornography usage, masturbation, grooming women, emotional affairs, prostitutes, sexual encounters, affairs and all types of escapades he has engaged in that she didn't factually know about.

Then, the next day she comes into session and she has put together her own realignment of these dates, work trips, him getting up late or early, paying more attention to his body, and putting blocks or passwords on devices. She begins to put together what I call the path of betrayal.

In the next several pages I want you to put together the path of your betrayal. Some events that have occurred may be obvious while others will be less clear but real nonetheless.

In dating, were there any red flags you had about his character? If so, write these down here:

____

____

____

____

____

____

____

____

____

____

During the dating period, were there weird instances that occurred with women that got explained away? If so, write them down here:

____

____

____

____

____

____

____

____

____

____

____

During the dating period, were there conversations about pornography or masturbation? If so, what were these?

During the dating period, did he have female friends that were different or he was unwilling to end when asked by you to end these relationships? If so write these here.

In the marriage, were there periods of time in which he was consistently critical of you? If so, write these below.

In the marriage, were there periods of time you just couldn't do anything right? If so, write them out below.

In the marriage, were there changes in your sex life or unusual requests that he made? When did these occur?

In the marriage, were there periods where it seemed he was less interested in sex with you? If so, write them below.

In the marriage, was he involved in projects, volunteering or other activities that took him away from the house regularly? If so, write them below.

In the marriage, were there women that you felt uncomfortable with him being in a relationship? If so, write your experiences here.

In the marriage, were there periods of what felt like increased or unnecessary traveling occurring? If so, write your experiences here.

In the marriage, were there issues or conflict around social media? If so, write your experiences here.

In the marriage, were there periods of just feeling married and alone? If so, write your experiences here.

If you had arguments over the years that didn't make sense and then he would leave for hours or longer write these here.

Hindsight is said to be 20/20. When it comes to betrayal it takes time to really understand or accept the total trauma of betrayal. The betrayal happens over time, an incident here, an incident there.

Men act differently when betraying their spouse/significant other. Some men pull away, others become critical and blaming so you don't get too close, while others keep acting exactly the same. Some are even more attentive with time, gifts, sex or other balancing activities toward you after or during betraying you.

In the below categories, write your experience of your husband or significant other during what you now know as the season(s) of betrayal.

Examples and times of pulling away or distancing himself from you during season(s) of betrayal.

Examples of him pushing you away or blaming you for how bad things are between you two:

Examples of him "acting so normal" during the season(s) of betrayal.

Examples of him being even more attentive to you during the season(s) of betrayal:

Counseling with so many women who have experienced betrayal trauma, I've seen many patterns in men who betray their partners. One pattern is how they use money during the season(s) of betrayal.

Write down your experiences with money over the season(s) of betrayal. Was he overly generous, overly controlling, overly stingy, or overly irresponsible? Write your experiences below.

Overly Generous:

Overly Controlling:

Overly Stingy:

Overly Irresponsible:

Money is also part of how many men betray their spouse. You rightfully so, feel hurt about every dollar spent on porn, strippers, sex services, hotel rooms, gifts to women and dates with women etc. This financial betrayal is painfully real for many women and can be symbolic or a challenge for them to absorb in this trauma.

In the space below, write about expenses you know that he paid out in some form or another to betray you. Write out what he spent it on, who he spent it on, how long he spent it and roughly how much.

What he spent it on:

Who he spent it on:

How long he spent money on betrayal:

Approximately how much money he spent on betraying you?

Events might have occurred through your relationship that at the time you may not have attached meaning to because you were unaware of the betrayal. Now, however, you can see the strangephone number, phone calls, websites, porn, odd events and his changes at the time that now give you a road map of betrayal.

This road map is definitely unique to you and your betrayal now has a journey. Write out here in the next few pages your unique betrayal journey. I want you to put the pieces of betrayal into one narrative.

Give this exercise your best try. This is the journey up to, but not including him getting caught or disclosing. Write your experiences, feelings, and intuitions leading up to the event of him getting caught. In the next section, you will address the trauma of the event.

Now that you have documented this pre-narrative of the betrayal up to the event, I want you to give voice to this betrayal journey. I want you to share this with a sponsor, therapist, spiritual mentor or a group member.

The date I shared the Betrayal Journey was on

____/____/____.

I started this Betrayal Journey with

____________________.

What I experienced in sharing my betrayal journey:

One more step. I've had many women tell me about the miraculous chain of events or how God Himself orchestrated events leading up to the husband getting caught or the husband disclosing his betrayal of you. If these situations occurred, write the narrative of the miraculous event(s) leading up to disclosure.

In the space below, write out a letter to God expressing feelings and thoughts about what it took to reveal this information to you.

The day I shared my narrative and letter to God was ____/____/____ *with* ____________________.

We've traveled pretty far together. We've covered the photographs of you being all in and trusting him. You have come to discover what an amazing woman you've been in this marriage or relationship. In the last section we covered the tremors of this earthquake of trauma that has hit your life and heart.

In this section we're going to walk together through one of the worst moments and worst day of your life. You've been betrayed. Many times I've sat with women receiving information from her husband or partner about how long, how many, who, and the various ways he has betrayed her. I've sat there as she processes his accounting of his misdeeds, seeing the reality of the situation go from her head to her toes. I've been there when her soul goes blank. I've been there as she screams "No! No!" I've been there to witness her struggle. I've seen countless times the trauma of all traumas devastate a woman's heart, spirit, and mind.

I know you've been through uncommunicable pain and trauma. I've spent many hours every week witnessing this happening or hearing a precious, good woman recounting her day of betrayal.

When you're experiencing the retraumatization of the accounting of the betrayal, so much is happening to you all at once. The past, present, and future as you knew it is now colliding with a totally different and horrible reality. You are now faced with the new reality of his choice to betray you over the course of the marriage or relationship.

Now that you had some time and distance from this day, I want to go back through this event so you can process, feel, and connect to your body. This is your time to record your trauma.

For some women, recording their trauma has helped them put this multidimensional trauma in perspective and helped them move out of the photograph of that moment into the movie of their current life.

Let's go frame-by-frame over your day of betrayal. Each frame will be different for you. If you feel you're having experiences you need support with during this section, feel free to reach out to the women you're using for support.

Your Betrayal Day

Write out what the earlier part of your day was like prior to the trauma. (i.e., picking up children, working, yoga, running errands)

What were some of your thoughts and feelings during this day prior to the trauma?

Were there proceeding events that occurred prior to disclosure or getting caught which happened? (i.e., phone call from another person, finding an email, text etc.) If so, write down any of these events or prior to disclosure or him getting caught.

Just to be clear, disclosure involves your spouse/significant other fully sharing his infidelity and transgressions. You're not presenting him with any ideas or questions. He will sit you down and explain to you how he has been betraying you.

"Getting caught" is any version in which evidence, data, questioning him, or proof of betrayal preceeds him in anyway towards being honest about his betrayal(s).

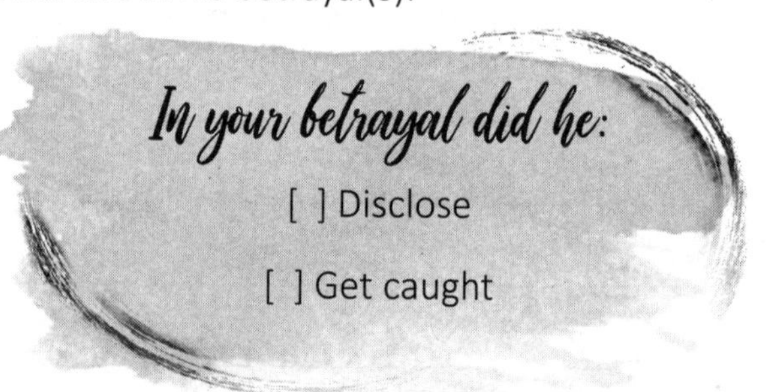

The event of trauma happens in a real place at a real time. I liken this to a car wreck. This wreck happened on such and such a day and such and such a time.

The time of my betrayal trauma event was roughly what time of the day?

____

Where were you when you received the information of being betrayed?

____

If you were in your home, what room? Were you sitting, if so where? If not where was your body? In what position, (be specific)?

Do you remember what you were wearing that day of your betrayal?

Where was he sitting or standing?

Were there any other persons involved during the event of getting the information of your betrayal? If so, who and what was their purpose for being there?

Now, let's explore the betrayal event. This is where the information of you being betrayed is starting to come forth.

Who started the conversation?

What was being discovered?

What did he actually say?

What started to happen to your body? (i.e., shaking, coldness, crying, screaming)

What were some of your immediate statements?

How do you remember him responding to you?

How long did this go on?

What else did you learn as this disclosure unfolded?

What events happened after disclosure? (i.e., I left, he left, I did....)

What were some of your immediate thoughts when he disclosed his betrayal?

What image(s) flashed through your brain during the disclosure?

What was happening to your body during this disclosure?

When do you remember being able to feel your body again after disclosure?

Sadly, some men dribble out disclosure. Rarely do they give you enough facts (not details) of their betrayal. They rarely say it started three years into marriage; it involved pornography, masturbation, chat rooms, three one-time random emotional affairs, and two prostitutes—the last time being six weeks ago.

Since so many men dribble out disclosure, many of you that have been betrayed have had to deal with on-going or multiple disclosures rather than receiving all the information at one time. Many of you have made your spouse/significant other promise "that's everything" only to find out in a later disclosure or a polygraph that there was more.

If you've had multiple disclosures, write out what else you learned and approximately how far apart from the original disclosure. (i.e., three weeks later I found out about a girl at the gym)

1

2

3

4

5

6

Add these events to your narrative and share the subsequent disclosure with a support person. You've completed a lot of work in this section of the workbook. Take time and write out for yourself, in the space below what your experience was in this section.

You might need additional pages than the ones provided here and that is fine. We've discussed your disclosure or betrayal event in some detail. I want you to write your disclosure event out in one narrative.

The day I shared my narrative and letter to God was ____/____/____ with ________________________.

My experience of sharing my betrayal event was:

The consequences of being betrayed by your husband or significant other are very far reaching. The pain is real regardless of how aware or unaware your husband or significant other may or may not be. Your intuition will affirm to you that this betrayal is a really big deal, affecting your past, present and future. You intuitively feel the cracks spreading through the various aspects of your life and being.

Let me be perfectly clear—your pain is real, your pain is valid, and you'll process this pain of the deepest betrayal of your life in your own unique way.

In the following pages, we'll focus on the consequences that you've uniquely experienced. I want to warn you that as you go through these pages you may experience a heightening of the pain you have in areas of your life. You may also become aware of pain you've yet to experience or didn't have the language to put these areas of pain into words.

You're a strong woman. Your Intentionally addressing the pain and consequences of betrayal is most likely the better, quicker, and more intelligent way to heal from betrayal.

Categories of consequences fall into three major areas: external consequences, internal consequences, and your relationship with your husband or significant other.

External Consequences:

External Consequences are those consequences that have impact in relationships or other areas outside of your marriage or relationship. Separating these categories is in no way prioritizing the pain in your trauma. You'll have variations of impact in all categories of the pain from the betrayal you've experienced.

Places: In some instances, the betrayal has impacted how you view and feel about certain places. If he acted out in betrayal of you in other countries, cities, hotels/motels; taken her to restaurants, shopping, even your house,. then these places may feel defiled to you. These places can also trigger you about the events that happened there. In the spaces below, list these places that affect you.

Places far away from you.

1. ______
2. ______
3. ______
4. ______
5. ______
6. ______
7. ______
8. ______
9. ______
10. ______

Places close to you.

1. ______
2. ______
3. ______
4. ______
5. ______
6. ______
7. ______
8. ______
9. ______
10. ______

Social Events:

Social events that he attended with the other woman or women. Feeling like a fake going anywhere socially or just not wanting to be with him, also not wanting to experience him visiting/flirting/grooming anyone in your presence and many other reasons social events are now difficult for you.

In your own words write out for yourself the reason why social events are now difficult for you.

Which social events are now really a challenge for you?

1.________________ 6.________________

2.________________ 7.________________

3.________________ 8.________________

4.________________ 9.________________

Finances:

Partners who have been betrayed feel different as to how finances have been involved. In the space below, write how your finances have been impacted because of the betrayal.

His finances were impacted:

Our household finances have been impacted:

My present finances have been impacted:

The potential future impact on my finances:

Employment: How has his employment or business been impacted by his choice to betray?

How has your employment or business been impacted by his betrayal?

School:

If the partner of betrayal is a student, this could have a great impact on her as well. In the below spaces write out what impact his betrayal has had on your schooling or your education:

House of Worship:

Partners are impacted differently on how they now relate to their house of worship. If you have been impacted in this way, write out the why and how you feel in the place of worship after the betrayal:

Children's places or events:

Has his betrayal impacted any places where the children have been currently involved? (i.e., sports, school performance, day-to-day events)

People:

In this section, highlight the people or relationships that have been impacted by his choice to betray you. Fill in what you perceive to be the impact of any of the relationships listed below:

Your family:

His family:

Child #1 (name):

Child #2 (name):

Child #3 (name):

Child #4 (name):

Child #5 (name):

Your close friends:

His friends:

His friends that knew:

Women who knew:

Extended family:

Your brothers/sisters:

His brothers/sisters:

Your grandparents:

His grandparents:

Cousins/ nephews/ God- children:

Grand children:

Neighbors:

Family friends:

Children's friends:

People at place of worship:

Spiritual leaders:

Other:

Plans:

Sadly, finding out about betrayal is never timely. You were living your present life and planning future events together. In the spaces below write out present and future events that are or will be impacted because of the betrayal. (i.e., weddings, graduations, vacations)

Events impacted:

1.
2.
3.
4.
5.
6.
7.
8.
9.
10.

Future plans impacted:

1.
2.
3.
4.
5.
6.
7.
8.
9.
10.

Living arrangements:

For some partners of betrayal their living arrangement can become impacted. The husband/significant other can choose to leave or he may be asked or forced to leave. If your living arrangements were impacted by his choice to betray you, write your experience below.

In the next couple of pages or on a separate sheet of paper write your narrative on how betrayal has impacted your external life.

The day I shared my narrative and letter to God was ____/____/____ with ________________________.

In the book, *Partner Betrayal Trauma*, I made a very compelling case that you have experienced a unique form of PTSD (Post Traumatic Stress Disorder). You might not have experienced general PTSD (being attacked, shot, having your life threatened), but you experienced partner betrayal trauma and had your marriage and family life as you know it threatened, attacked or even killed.

I "partnerized" the symptom questions for the *Diagnostic and Statistical Manual*. Below write out your personal experience for each of these scenarios. Remember your experience of partner betrayal trauma will be unique to you and different from others.

When I found out about his behaviors I felt that my marriage and relationship with him was severely threatened or could end. Describe your experience:

____
____
____
____
____
____
____

My response to finding out his behavior included: Intense fear, Intense helplessness, Horror. Describe your experience:

____
____
____
____
____
____
____

Since finding out about his behavior I have had intrusive distressing thoughts. Describe your experience:

____
____
____
____
____
____
____

Since finding out about his behavior I have had intrusive distressing dreams. Describe your experience:

____
____
____
____
____
____
____

I have experienced reliving the experience of finding out about his behavior or what the behaviors were (i.e., flashbacks, illusions, hallucinations like you were actually there again.) This is not just a thought but feeling that you are actually there reliving the experience. Describe your experience:

____

____

____

____

____

____

____

I have experienced intense psychological distress when I have externally or internally been exposed to something that symbolizes or resembles his behavior. Describe your experience:

____

____

____

____

____

____

____

I have had efforts to avoid thoughts, feelings or conversations about his behavior after disclosure. Describe your experience:

____

____

____

____

____

____

____

I have had efforts to avoid activities, places or people that arouse recollections of his behavior. Describe your experience:

____

____

____

____

____

____

____

____

I have had inability to recall aspects of information about his behavior after discovery. Describe your experience:

____

____

____

____

____

____

____

____

I have experienced significant diminished interest or participation in significant activities after finding out about his behavior. Describe your experience:

____

____

____

____

____

____

____

After finding out about his behavior I have experienced feelings of detachment or estrangement from other people. Describe your experience:

Since finding out about his behavior I felt emotionally restricted? Describe your experience:

Since finding out about his behavior I have had a sense that my future has been shortened. Describe your experience:

Check off all the below that you have experienced since finding out about his behavior:

□ Difficulty falling asleep
□ Irritability or outbursts of anger
□ Difficulty concentrating
□ Hyper-vigilance
□ Exaggerated startled response

As a result of finding out about his behavior I have experienced significant distress of impairment in social, occupational or other important areas of functioning in my life. Describe your experience:

As you traveled through these pages you easily could conclude that you are having legitimate PTSD symptoms. This could provide a road map for specific issues and goals to resolve in therapy.

Triggers:

In PTSD a person can have the external environment provide something similar to your experience. Maybe you see something in a movie, television show or hear a friends story that parallels your experience. This can create extreme feelings for you.

When you are triggered you will need to have a protocol and follow this protocol to regain emotional stability. Remember your husband can consistently do this early in recovery. Below is a short list of some ideas:

- Call another women in recovery
- Pray
- Remove yourself and have a positive memory. Move your mind until your emotions follow.
- Practice the *Emotional Fitness* protocol and switch to another feeling
- Journal

Other things I know to do:

Here write out the protocol you will actually follow when you are triggered.

To whom will you be accountable to follow your protocol so you can self regulate your emotions at the times of being triggered.

If I consistently fail to use my protocol to self regulate I will go to which therapist specifically for tools and accountability to self regulate my emotions.

You cant prevent the environment from having "triggers". You can have a plan and work that plan so you and your body can navigate this in a safe and healthy manner.

Gaslighting:

This term has come to mean so many things. In short it is your husbands/significant others immature way of not taking responsibility, crazy making or blaming you for his behavior or bad choices.

Triggers, especially in the early months into your husband's healing, will likely happen. Remember he is often an adolescent emotionally moving toward becoming a mature man. Being male doesn't automatically make you a mature man.

What are your protocols when he "attempts" to gaslight you?

Who in your life is really good to talk with to get grounded in reality when gaslighting is "attempted"?

He can only attempt to gaslight you. In what ways has he gaslighted you before?

1.______________________________

2.______________________________

3.______________________________

4.______________________________

5.______________________________

6.______________________________

7.______________________________

8.______________________________

Most likely he will try to do this again. So create a protocol around those you have listed.

1.______________________________

2.______________________________

3.______________________________

4.______________________________

5.______________________________

6.______________________________

7.______________________________

8.______________________________

When he is gaslighting you he is emotionally unregulated and wants you to join his unregulated state. If you jump into this game, who is responsible for you becoming unregulated? Him or you? Why?

____

____

____

____

____

____

____

Distance making

Gaslighting is legitimate. However, if you are living with an intimacy anorexic what may feel like gaslighting is actually an intentional maneuver to create distance in the relationship. When an intimacy anorexic is feeling too close, that anxiety or fear of intimacy can create emotional regulation for him. He then will blame, be critical, withhold love, withhold praise, withhold sex, become angry or totally silent in order to create distance again.

The motive is totally different than gaslighting and is way more intentional. Gaslighting is generally an immature response to life aimed at you because you're there or because they don't want to take responsibility for something. Distance making is intentional. There will be specific strategies that are:

1. Exclusive to you
2. Effective at creating distance
3. Repetitive.

Here you will have to identify the agenda. We call it the Block Punch: You say, "I am feeling distance. What can you do to nurture me?" If he moves toward you, he is not being anorexic. If he continues to blame or pull away he is emotionally unregulated and don't join in.

Is your spouse an intimacy anorexic?

___Yes ___No

Can you see examples of intentional distance making in your relationship in the past? If so list examples.

1.____

2.____

3.____

4.____

5.____

6.____

7.____

8.____

If he is an intimacy anorexic you will need a whole tool kit. I recommend the *Married & Alone: Healing Exercises for Spouses* for this part of your recovery.

Partner betrayal trauma is real and the PTSD symptoms you have most likely experienced are as well. Partner recovery is about moving toward a solution. If you feel you need specific help around this one aspect of your recovery reach out for more support.

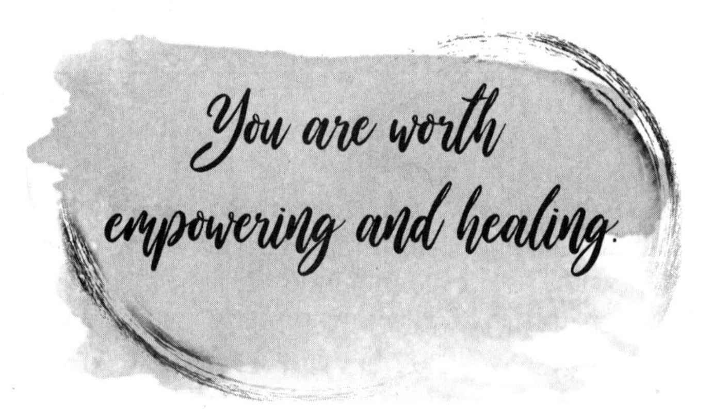

Internal consequences of his betrayal is when the eye can't see but the heart feels the pain of trauma. Betrayal has many consequences. Some can be languaged and some are just experienced. In this section, you will explore your internal pain, your heart, your strength, your emotions, sexuality, and your general sense of being after the trauma of betrayal.

Emotions: When trauma occurs, your emotions can be hugely impacted. Each woman is unique about how trauma affects them. For some, feelings of uncontrollable anger arise (i.e., fear, anxiety, mistrust, rage, controlling behavior) For other women some emotions become a challenge to feel. They encounter having challenges feeling some feelings (i.e., joy, safety, confidence, respect).

The feelings I've had challenges with managing since the betrayal trauma are:

1.________________ 6.________________

2.________________ 7.________________

3.________________ 8.________________

4.________________ 9.________________

5.________________ 10.________________

Spiritual betrayal can affect the way we think, feel or behave toward God. Betrayal can also impact our spirit.

Cognitively: Cognitively is the way we think, our conversation ability, and our ability to make decisions. In the below spaces, write how you have been cognitively affected by the betrayal:

Sexually: One of the areas you can be the most greatly impacted by betrayal is sexually. You can feel this impact with intrusive thoughts, feelings about your sexuality you have never felt before, body-image issues, and performance and pleasure changes that occur after the betrayal trauma. In the spaces below, write out how sexually the betrayal has impacted you. If you need more space, use additional paper to write the impact on your sexuality including sexual interaction and ability to connect after the betrayal trauma.

Social self: Betrayal trauma can impact the way you feel about people in general. Betrayal trauma can impact you or change your behavior from how you were prior to the betrayal trauma. In the space below, write how socially the betrayal has impacted you.

Parentally: Sadly, partners of betrayal trauma have told me, "I'm just not the mom I was before." Betrayal impacts all of who you are as a woman. Parenting is definitely a very important part of who you are as a woman. In the spaces below, write out how betrayal has impacted you as a parent.

Physically: Trauma definitely affects the body. For some, you might gain/lose weight, others sleep a lot or experience insomnia, you could feel energy changes, have an exacerbation of any illness, experience less coordination which can lead to falls or other incidents. Your body's reaction to betrayal trauma are uniquely yours. However in the *Partner Betrayal Trauma* book, we made a list of symptoms we have measured. You can circle any of these you have experienced.

Stomach pain *Back pain* *Joint pain*
Menstrual pain *During Intercourse pain* *Headaches*
Chest pain *Dizziness* *Fainting*
Racing heart *Shortness of breath* *Constipation*
Nausea

Here I would like you to make a list of doctors you need to see. Remember to include cortisol levels and hormone panels. These are important because of the amount of the trauma your body has experienced.

In the space below, write out what you believe has been the impact the betrayal trauma has had on your body.

Depression: Depression is a reality for many partners of betrayal trauma. Below is a check list for depression. If several of these apply to you, be honest and add this to your healing journey.

- *Poor appetite or overeating*
- *Low energy or fatigue*
- *Poor concentration or difficulty making decisions*
- *Suicidial thoughts*
- *Diminished interest or pleasure in most activities*
- *Unable to sleep or over sleeping*
- *Feelings of restlessness or being slowed down*
- *Feelings of hopelessness*
- *Depressed mood*

Dreams: Here I want to differentiate between two types of dreams. There are the dreams you experience when you sleep. These dreams can be impacted as you process your betrayal trauma. The other type of dreams are those you had for yourself, your marriage, and your family. Trauma can impact how you feel about or believe in these dreams any longer. These dreams that you may have had for decades can become tainted by the betrayal trauma. In the space below, write out how the trauma has impacted your dreams.

Dreams at night while sleeping:

Dreams I had for myself:

Dreams I had for our marriage:

Dreams I had for him:

Dreams I had for my family:

Narrative: Inside all of us we believe a story about ourselves that is considered our narrative. In the space below, write out your narrative about who you are and how you felt about yourself PRIOR to the betrayal. Then write a second narrative about who you are and how you feel about yourself now AFTER the betrayal.

My narrative of myself before the betrayal:

My narrative of myself after the betrayal:

As you compare/contrast these narratives of before and after what are some things that stick out to you?

Since trauma and women who experience trauma/betrayal trauma are unique, the internal impacts are also distinctive to each person. If you have other internal impacts you feel need to be identified, use the space below to highlight these specific areas of impact that have yet to be addressed in previous sections.

You have traveled the internal road of the impact of partner betrayal trauma. I'm very proud of you for all this challenging work you're achieving. In the next pages, or on a separate tablet, write out a narrative about how partners betrayal has impacted you internally.

I shared my internal narrative with ____________________

on _____/_____/_____.

As a partner experiencing betrayal trauma there's a "him." He may be your husband or significant other, but his choices have deeply affected the way you feel, think or relate to him on so many levels. These changes are a direct result of his choice or ongoing choices to betray you. In this section, you will explore some of the impact this trauma has had on you as it has affected how you relate to him. In this section, you'll do a compare and contrast of before and after the trauma. The contrast can significantly impact the trauma has had on you.

You've been sharing your heart and emotions with "him" for years or decades. Write out how you believe you behaved with your husband/significant other prior to any knowledge of his betrayal.

____

____

____

____

____

____

____

After betrayal, the way you share or don't share your heart and feelings can be different. Write out how difficult or easy it is to share your heart and feelings after the betrayal.

____

____

____

____

____

____

____

Physically: This is not about sexual interaction, rather just how difficult or easy it is to feel comfortable around him (i.e.,kissing, spontaneous kissing, etc.) What was your behavior around your husband/ significant other physically prior to the betrayal?

After the betrayal trauma, write how comfortable you are physically with your husband?

Spiritually: The spiritual connection to a husband/significant other is one of the most intimate connections you'll ever experience with another human being. Describe your spiritual relationship with your husband/ significant other prior to the betrayal.

Describe your spiritual relationship with your husband/significant other after the betrayal.

Sexual: This is by far the most intimate relationship you can have with anyone. In marriage or a committed relationship this is supposed to be sacred and special. Describe your feelings about your sexual relationship with him prior to betrayal.

Describe your sexual relationship after the betrayal.

Money: As a couple, money is an area in which you should have mutual trust and ability to share together. How was your relationship with him as it related to money prior to the betrayal?

How is your relationship with money with him after the betrayal?

Parenting: If you're parents you have quite a interdependent, intensive, on-going relationship with each other as you parent. Describe your relationship with him as a parent prior to knowledge of the betrayal.

Describe your relationship as a parent after the betrayal.

Narrative: Before the knowledge of his betrayal, you had a way of thinking about your husband/ significant other. This way of thinking about him is how you would describe him to others as well as to yourself. In the following space write out your general story or narrative about him prior to betrayal.

In the space below write your general narrative of your husband/significant other after the betrayal.

As stated previously, your betrayal trauma experience is unique to you. In the space below write out other ways in which you believe his betrayal has impacted the way you relate to him:

As you look over this last section and you review the impact his betrayal has affected the way you relate to him, write down some of the feelings you're having.

1. ______________________
2. ______________________
3. ______________________
4. ______________________
5. ______________________
6. ______________________
7. ______________________
8. ______________________
9. ______________________
10. ______________________

In the previous section, you wrote a narrative about the impact of the betrayal trauma you're experiencing. Next, write out the narrative about how this betrayal trauma has impacted the way you relate to him.

I shared this narrative with  ______________________

on ____/____/____

Losses for the partner of betrayal trauma are also significant and often ongoing. Losses are things that you're not going to get back at all or for a period of time. For example, the consequence or loss from betrayal is fidelity. A result of your loss from betrayal trauma is being able to say "we" have been faithful to each other. You might have integrity and fidelity but as a couple, "we" no longer do.

Losses are usually unseen until bumped into by life or through processing the trauma. In the following pages, you'll have the opportunity to acknowledge and validate to yourself several of the losses of which you are currently aware.

After you identify losses in the various areas, you'll see listed the stages of grief. As you acknowledge a loss, circle the stage of grief you most identify with while you're completing this section. The stages of grief are shock, denial, anger, bargaining, sadness, and acceptance.

Trust: Write down your losses as they pertain to trust. My losses are:

Safety: Write down your losses as they pertain to safety. My losses are:

Emotionally: Write down your losses as they pertain to your emotions. My losses are:

Spiritually: Write down your losses as they pertain to spiritual aspects. My losses are:

Sexually: Write down your losses as they pertain to sex. My losses are:

Financially: Write down your losses as they pertain to finances. My losses are:

Family: Write down your losses as they pertain to family. My losses are:

Children: Write down your losses as they pertain to children. My losses are:

Socially: Write down your losses as they pertain to social aspects. My losses are:

Rituals as a couple: Write down your losses as they pertain to rituals as a couple. My losses are:

Rituals as a family: Write down your losses as they pertain to rituals as a family. My losses are:

Losses from the past: Write down your losses as they pertain to losses from the past. My losses are:

Losses in the present: Write down your losses as they pertain to losses in the present. My losses are:

Losses in the future: Write down your losses as they pertain to losses to the future. My losses are:

Going through your losses is definitely painful. These losses are real and many of them are permanent because of his betrayal. The process of grieving will be ongoing. The grieving of each individual loss will take time. Come back to this section over time to see how your grief is progressing.

In the next two pages write out the summary or narrative about your losses from his betrayal.

I shared my losses narrative with ____________________

on _____/_____/_____

Anger from Betrayal

When you've been betrayed by your partner you'll feel anger. You may choose to hold your anger inside, share it with others, over-exercise, stay in bed all day, or have any number of responses that reflect your anger. Anger is an inevitable emotion and partner betrayal trauma is the deepest trauma you can experience.

This type of trauma affects every aspect of your life. The previous sections of this workbook exposed some of the far-reaching consequences and losses you have experienced. In this section, you'll address the betrayal trauma and other traumas you might have experienced.

You need to evaluate how you have been handling anger. Below is a list based on my experience hearing the hearts of betrayal-traumatized women. Circle the actions you've been using or used in the past.

Yelling	Crying	Exercising
Controlling	Eating	Praying
Silence	Stuffing	Talking to girlfriends
Sleep	Sarcasm	Journaling
Withholding sex	Shopping	______Other
Disrespecting him	Humiliating Him	______Other

Before we delve into the anger you feel about your husband or significant other, we'll go through your trauma history. If there were other individuals who caused trauma in your life, list their names below. We'll come back to this list after we complete some anger work about your husband.

Others who created trauma for me are:

1.______________________ 6.______________________

2.______________________ 7.______________________

3.______________________ 8.______________________

4.______________________ 9.______________________

5.______________________ 10.______________________

I think I've established in earlier sections the vast, multilayered, and multidimensional impact this partner betrayal has had on your external and internal life. Simply chatting with anyone alone is not going to address all this anger.

The following exercise has helped literally thousands of women. I've witnessed firsthand in my office the before and after of women doing this exercise exactly as I have asked. These women vary in age, color, religion, region of origin, and every single one of them have a unique and individual personality. Other than having a heart issue or health-preventing issue (if so, speak to your doctor before doing this exercise), I highly recommend you follow the steps I lay out and withhold judgement or opinion about this exercise until afterward. Some of the women with the greatest results had the most resistance to the anger exercise.

Step one: Write an anger letter to your husband/significant other that he will never see, hear or read.

This letter is the stuff you would say hitting your steering wheel—an all-out anger, rage-filled letter speaking to what he has done to you, your life, and the family. Don't hold anything back. Feel free to use any language you want. Do not in any way go toward forgiveness or try to spiritualize this letter. That all comes later.

Remember under NO circumstance does he see, hear or read this letter! He is likely not mature enough to empathize with your pain (watch the DVD *When You Marry A Child Don't Expect A Man Right Away*). You reading this letter to him Will Not help him "get it." [If you want him to "get it," have him watch *Helping Her Heal*, a DVD for men. This DVD is the most helpful resource available to help him understand your pain.]

Step Two: Read your letter out loud to yourself.

Step Three: You'll need a safe bat, racquet or something that won't break that you can hit a mattress with.

Then, warm up a little using small, medium, large, extra-large hits on a bed (don't use the bed you sleep on).

Step Four: Go ballistic. Yell, scream, and hit. Be as loud as you want and need to be.

Trauma wasn't pretty going into your spirit, soul, and body and it's not pretty going out.

Give yourself an hour after you write the letter for when you do stop. If you want a friend or sponsor in the home for safety or processing that's fine. Most women prefer to be totally alone when they let this very intense rage out of the body. The body needs to be part of healing the trauma.

I finished writing my anger letter on ____/____/_____.

I finished doing my anger work by hitting and letting it out ____/____/_____.

Keep these two dates as close together as possible. You do not want to write the letter and hold that in your body. I highly recommend you do the anger exercise immediately after the anger letter is written.

In the space below, write out your experience with the anger work. Were there any themes that came out doing the anger exercise? If so, add this to your experience.

My experience with the anger work was:

____

____

____

____

____

____

Now if you are one of the many women who have experienced multiple traumas throughout your life then I want you to do the same process steps 1-4 for each person who has traumatized you. Each person is a unique trauma and each anger experience will also be different. The women who do this cleansing of their body and soul from trauma never regret it.

You don't deserve to carry trauma in your body. You may want to make yourself accountable to a woman to make sure you continue the anger work for everyone on the list.

I shared my anger work and experience with ____________________

on ____/____/_____

In the space below, again write down the names of the people who have traumatized you. Then write the date you finished the anger work concerning them.

1. *Name*____________ *I told*____________ *on* ____/____/____ *about my anger work and experience.*
2. *Name*____________ *I told*____________ *on* ____/____/____ *about my anger work and experience.*
3. *Name*____________ *I told*____________ *on* ____/____/____ *about my anger work and experience.*
4. *Name*____________ *I told*____________ *on* ____/____/____ *about my anger work and experience.*
5. *Name*____________ *I told*____________ *on* ____/____/____ *about my anger work and experience.*
6. *Name*____________ *I told*____________ *on* ____/____/____ *about my anger work and experience.*
7. *Name*____________ *I told*____________ *on* ____/____/____ *about my anger work and experience.*
8. *Name*____________ *I told*____________ *on* ____/____/____ *about my anger work and experience.*
9. *Name*____________ *I told*____________ *on* ____/____/____ *about my anger work and experience.*
10. *Name*____________ *I told*____________ *on* ____/____/____ *about my anger work and experience.*

Now, write out a summary of your experience doing the anger work on all the people who created trauma in your life.

I shared this with ____________________

on _____/_____/_____

Boundaries, which for reasons I don't always comprehend, seem to vary for each person in the whole partners movement. As a partner of betrayal trauma, having a clear understanding of what a boundary is or is not can be really helpful as you navigate your healing in the context of a marriage or relationship.

Write out what your current behavior boundary is and the purpose of a boundary in a relationship.

The purpose of a boundary is to maintain equitable respect for both partners. The United States has a boundary across Canada. The boundary states that our land is here while yours is there. We will respect your laws and land and you will respect ours.

Boundaries that are conveyed correctly, comes from a heart of respect not fear. Before we get to that, let's first explore the topic of assertiveness.

Assertiveness

One of my first trainings as a master level counselor had to do with being assertive. Some people are challenged with either being too aggressive or too passive. Assertiveness brings both parties back to the middle of too aggressive or too passive. To be assertive is not negative, in fact it is quite the opposite. Here are the key points to assertiveness:

1. *Aggressive is respect me. I don't respect/value you (I am greater).*
2. *Passive is I don't respect/value myself. I respect/value you (you are greater).*
3. *I respect and value myself and respect and value you at the same time (assertive).*

With just those short definitions, how would you define how your husband/significant other has been with you:

Before the betrayal — *Aggressive* *Assertive* *Passive*

After the betrayal — *Aggressive* *Assertive* *Passive*

How would you say that you have been toward your husband/significant other?

Before the betrayal — *Aggressive* *Assertive* *Passive*

After the betrayal — *Aggressive* *Assertive* *Passive*

In the space below, write your thoughts about the level of respect that existed and currently exists between the two of you.

____

____

____

____

____

____

____

If respect is not mutual, boundaries will definitely be a challenge. I've seen many situations in which one person in the couple was passive and then became extremely aggressive after the trauma. I've also seen situations in which one person in the couple was aggressive and then became passive after the trauma. In each scenario, the foundation of disrespect is still alive—we just switched who is the bully in the marriage or relationship.

Does your marriage or relationship mirror this change in direction by either person? If so, write about it in the space below.

If you would like more information on assertiveness training, Google it or look up the subject on Amazon. If you are both not assertive, all sorts of aggressive, passive aggressive, disrespectful words and behavior with resentment could build up.

System

Marriage and significant relationships are many things but one thing they are is a system. The couple creates systems of beliefs and behaviors both functional and dysfunctional to survive in the marriage. Let's discuss a few systems of marriage.

Adult/Adult system: Both are mature, not addicted, living life well, responsible, keep their word and respect each other for the most part.

Adult/Child: One person is mature often over functioning in the relationship because the other is immature, lies, doesn't keep their word, doesn't follow through, isn't responsible, can be addicted, and generally blames instead of taking responsibility. If the male is the adult, this is a daddy/daughter relationship. If the female is the adult this is mommy/son relationship.

Child/Child: both are immature, addicted, won't take responsibility, fear change and blame is a lifestyle. This emotionally-based marriage/relationship has many challenges on many fronts.

Based upon the above, in the space below, write which system you had before the trauma and why you believe this:

____

____

____

____

____

____

____

____

____

____

____

____

____

____

____

____

Describe the system you now have with your spouse/partner and why you believe this:

Why do you believe understanding the system of marriage affects boundaries?

Although there are exceptions, the marital/relationship system that I see most often in my office is the parent/child system. Most often, the wife is exhausted from over-functioning and the husband is largely oblivious.

To be fair, I deal a lot with intimacy anorexia and sex addicts. These men are generally spiritually, emotionally, morally immature because the addictive process has stunted them. To provide perspective, I have seen thousands of these men fully mature and become great husbands and dads after recovery.

However, for that to happen, the system of mommy/child has to change for boundaries to be effective. The mommy/child will need to maintain and hold to set boundaries. Without establishing boundaries, she will fluctuate between reacting either aggressively or passive aggressively in response to the spouse who is attempting to manipulate, minimize, and continue to deny the issues. This behavior is commonly referred to as gaslighting.

A mommy/child marriage is dysfunctional. Regardless as to why or how this system evolved, it's dysfunctional and could be disastrous if behaviors are implemented from this system.

Change

Men make men! I have had at least a thousand partners of betrayal trauma tell me "Dr. Weiss I have told him exactly what you just said and he heard you but never hears me." That is because men make men. You can't ever make a man out of your husband or significant other. Years of research support this truth yet many women still believe if they try harder, smarter, louder, or withhold he will change. You are 100% powerless over any man in your life.

I know this is challenging but what do you think and feel about the idea that men make men?

There are counselors, especially in the field of dealing with betrayed partners, who have perpetuated the idea of just changing the dominant person. Giving her a voice (which is good) sets her up with unlimited power to tell him what he can and cannot do. This perpetrates the dysfunction of the mommy/child relationship and all the resentments that go along with that system.

Counselors and coaches mean well but they're also people who may be dysfunctional. I tell my male sex addicts that if they're looking for a counselor, ask the counselor when was the last time they masturbated or viewed porn. If the counselor can't or won't answer that, leave the office.

In the same way I have had female counselors tell women to not have sex with him until x,y,z occurs. I tell this woman the same thing and tell her to ask that counselor how often she has sex with her husband, how often does she initiate sex with him? And how engaged she is during sex? If that counselor can't or won't answer, she shouldn't be telling you what to do. So be wise as you get counsel about your betrayal trauma.

We want to change the mommy/child system, not perpetuate it. We want to move to a place of mutual respect in establishing boundaries. The below illustrates a point by using a recovery behavior but you insert any action such as raising your voice, spending issues, etc. here.

1. Establish the behavior to be addressed for him (together).
2. He creates a consequence for himself and a time to complete the consequence.
3. Establish who he will be accountable for this behavior.
4. You agree with the consequence or negotiate an agreed-upon consequence (mutual respect).
5. If the undesired behavior happens and he completes the consequence and tells his accountability male, then he doesn't need to be punished by you. Instead, he punished himself. (Adult behavior).
6. If he does undesired specified behavior, acts like a child and won't do his consequence, then you have an established boundary for yourself that you can achieve without his cooperation and you implement it.

Real example:

1. Both agree masturbation is not acceptable.
2. He sets up a consequence of picking up trash on a street or highway for 3 hours. You agree. He says he will be accountable to Bob. You agree.
3. He masturbates, tells Bob, picks up trash, we are done.
4. If he masturbates but doesn't do consequence within the pre-established 72 hours, you do your estalished boundary such as, stop doing his laundry for two weeks.

This avoids the whole scenario in which you have to react like you're still within the mommy/child system. Instead, as an adult, he agrees to punish himself for childish behaviors. Your boundary is that masturbation is unacceptable.

What Boundaries Are Not

Boundaries are based on respect. You only implement boundaries after he refuses to follow through. He will test you to see if you will follow through. Remember the mommy/child system has been in place a long time. Do everything you can to move toward an adult/adult relationship.

I wanted to take a few minutes to just quickly state what a boundary is not. A boundary is not:

1. A magic power to change him.
2. A promise you will be safe.
3. A promise he will grow up.
4. A way to punish him.
5. A way to control for your desired outcome.

Below, write what you think about those last five statements.

____

____

____

____

____

Boundaries can be challenging. After recovery, consequences and boundaries are set. Wait about a month to see if the system is changing. If it is changing do one, two but no more than three boundaries a month. If the system is changing:

1. He is stopping the behavior(s).
2. He completes his consequence, without you reminding him.
3. Blaming decreases as personal responsibility grows.
4. Mutual respect grows.

If after a month you don't see some changes, then the fight to keep the old system in place still exists. At this point in time, you'll want to seek a therapist to help recreate an adult/adult system.

In my book *Emotional Fitness*, I walk the reader through what we call the unchaining exercise. This exercise should only be completed if you completed the anger work in the previous section.

Trauma is complex, especially partner betrayal trauma. Discharging the anger helps the body move through the trauma. The unchaining exercise addresses the soul aspects of freeing yourself from the residue of trauma.

This exercise is not performed to get you to forgive him or anyone else on your trauma history list. This exercise shows you where you are in the forgiveness process without needing any participation from those who have traumatized you.

Generally, people who traumatize others are in object relationships or are very immature. Wanting them to understand or empathize can hold you up and still gives them unnecessary power in your heart and life.

Unchaining

Unchaining yourself can be an invaluable experience. It is an exercise and act of your will you do to free yourself from the events and pain of the past.

Unchaining gives you an opportunity to see where you really are in forgiving those who have hurt you. I have done this many times in my life when dealing with my past. I have also done this in current situations that demanded I deal with anger in order to unchain myself.

Before I get to the specifics of the exercise, I want to expose you to some myths about forgiving that I discussed in my book, *The 7 Love Agreements* (Siloam, 2005).

Myths

1. I must confront my perpetrator to offer him or her forgiveness.
2. My perpetrator must be repentant or broken to be forgiven.
3. My perpetrator must change before I can forgive.

These myths put the very powerful act of forgiveness on the person who caused the pain. That person may not be able to be located or worse, may still not have the maturity to own the darkness they have intentionally or unintentionally released in your life.

The Truth

1. They do not even have to acknowledge, in any way, the pain they caused you for you to forgive them.
2. They do not have to repent or be broken for you to forgive them.
3. They do not have to change for you to forgive them.

The unclogging exercise removes all the power from the people who hurt you and gives you the power to unchain yourself and release forgiveness back to you. For me, the fact that I had the power to forgive and live, and I did not have to wait for others to do this was a powerful paradigm shift.

You too do not have to wait one more day to truly forgive the people from your past who have legitimately hurt you. As you walk through this exercise, you must simply be authentic. Even if you are unable to forgive at the time of the exercise, it will help you see where you are and that you can try again in the future.

I want to go through the unchaining exercise in which you will be role playing your husband/significant other.

I day I did my unchaining exercise on him or my significant other was ____/____/____

In the space below write out what you experienced in the exercise.

____

____

____

____

____

____

____

____

____

____

____

____

____

____

If you were able to forgive that is great progress. If you are still in the process, give it a month and try again. You might want accountability so put it on your phone and let someone know. Write below when you were able to actually forgive him. Be patient with yourself and just come back monthly until you are able to unchain yourself.

Remember that list of those on your trauma history? The ones on your list that you already have completed the anger work on? I want you to also do the unchaining exercise on them.

Place their names below and the dates you first did the unchaining and the date you forgave.

Person	First attempt	Forgave
1.________________	____/____/____	____/____/____
2.________________	____/____/____	____/____/____
3.________________	____/____/____	____/____/____
4.________________	____/____/____	____/____/____
5.________________	____/____/____	____/____/____
6.________________	____/____/____	____/____/____
7.________________	____/____/____	____/____/____
8.________________	____/____/____	____/____/____
9.________________	____/____/____	____/____/____
10.________________	____/____/____	____/____/____

When you are completed with your list, write your experience with unchaining in the space below.

____

____

____

____

____

____

____

____

When you are a partner of betrayal trauma, trust is going to be a journey. You might decide not to work on trust and instead end the relationship legally, emotionally or sexually.

However, if your desire is to repair the marriage or significant relationship then trust is a journey. There are two aspects of this journey. The first aspect of the journey is him maturing and becoming trustworthy. You give trust and trust will most likely be repeatedly fractured.

The second part of the journey of trust is when you give trust. Extending trust will be a process and an often silent event but you'll know when it happens.

Let's first touch upon the second largest road block to rebuilding trust. (The first is him not becoming trustworthy.)

Meaning

In the DVD/download *Unstuck*, I address how people who betray are living in an object world. The rules for being in an object world are:

1. People have no value.
2. You can lie, cheat, steal, manipulate, use or abandon because they have no value.
3. When a person is operating in an object-oriented system, they're living, deciding, feeling and behaving as if they were playing a video game.

The problem is almost every woman who has been betrayed operates from a relational reality. The rules for relational reality are:

1. Don't cheat.
2. Don't lie.
3. Don't steal.
4. Don't hurt others.
5. And a whole list of do's and don'ts that protect and reinforce the value of the soul of each person.

Even at a quick glance you can see these are two totally different operating systems. You will try to understand his insane choices with your relational rules, which honestly don't apply. You will give his behavior meaning that the behavior doesn't have.

Let me give you two very common examples of misplaced meaning. You're relational so you wouldn't have sex with someone you don't truly love. You're unaware of the object-relationship perspective so you project that he loves these women—even if they were prostitutes he simply must care about them. The cold truth is he didn't love them, he used them.

The second common "meaning" you apply to the situation is he told them he loved them—you have it as evidence on his phone, email or card that he bought her. Because you wouldn't tell a man you love him unless you actually did. You apply this same way of thinking to your husband/significant other. Again, unaware of the object-processing perspective that your husband/significant other is capable of, you project your relational reality onto him and believe he loves them. Truth is, just conning them to keep getting sex from them, that's it. You can't believe this so you go back to giving more "meaning" to the situation than he ever did and you believe that he loves them.

Here is why I say meaning is the second problem blocking you from moving toward trust. As the partner of betrayal who is relational, you're trying to rebuild trust based on your misplaced meaning of "he loves them," which isn't true. When you're creating a bigger meaning, it can be like climbing a mountain that grows as you're climbing. If this is unclear to you, please watch the *Unstuck* DVD as it can be a game changer for you accepting something instead of trying to understand his behavior through your relational lens.

It might be easier for you to forgive someone who manipulated and used someone for sex than it would be trying to forgive him for "loving them." Once you can move through how the meaning you're applying is incorrect, accepting and rebuilding trust can be easier.

A Big Topic

Trust is a big topic in partner betrayal trauma. Trust is one of those multifaceted, multidimensional aspects of marriage or a committed relationship. Most partners are "all in" their marriage or relationship and they believed their spouse or significant other was as well.

Since trust is multidimensional, I put together a way to solve different areas of your trust before and after the trauma.

Trust is not all or nothing in a complex relationship like marriage or a committed relationship. You might still completely trust him in several areas of your relationship and have zero trust in other areas.

That's the journey of trust—find where it's weak and create options to rebuild trust. Let's start this journey by seeing what areas of trust are stronger or weaker than other areas in your relationship.

Trust Questions

1. Prior to your knowledge of betrayal, did you trust your husband/significant other emotionally?

___1 ___2 ___3 ___4 ___5 ___6 ___7 ___8 ___9 ___10

Not at all *Totally*

2. Prior to your knowledge of betrayal, did you trust your husband/significant other?

___1 ___2 ___3 ___4 ___5 ___6 ___7 ___8 ___9 ___10

Not at all *Totally*

3. Prior to your knowledge of betrayal, did you trust your husband/significant other spiritually?

___1 ___2 ___3 ___4 ___5 ___6 ___7 ___8 ___9 ___10

Not at all *Totally*

4. Prior to your knowledge of betrayal, did you trust your husband/significant other in social situations?

___1 ___2 ___3 ___4 ___5 ___6 ___7 ___8 ___9 ___10

Not at all *Totally*

5. Prior to your knowledge of betrayal, did you trust your husband/significant other sexually?

___1 ___2 ___3 ___4 ___5 ___6 ___7 ___8 ___9 ___10

Not at all *Totally*

6. Prior to your knowledge of betrayal, did you trust your husband/significant other financially?

___1 ___2 ___3 ___4 ___5 ___6 ___7 ___8 ___9 ___10

Not at all *Totally*

7. Prior to your knowledge of betrayal, did you trust your husband/significant other parenting?

___1 ___2 ___3 ___4 ___5 ___6 ___7 ___8 ___9 ___10

Not at all *Totally*

8. Prior to your knowledge of betrayal, did you trust your husband/significant other with general responsibilities?

___1 ___2 ___3 ___4 ___5 ___6 ___7 ___8 ___9 ___10

Not at all *Totally*

9. Prior to your knowledge of betrayal, did you trust your husband/significant other in other extended family relationships?

___1 ___2 ___3 ___4 ___5 ___6 ___7 ___8 ___9 ___10

Not at all *Totally*

10. Prior to your knowledge of betrayal, did you trust your husband/significant other to keep their word?

___1 ___2 ___3 ___4 ___5 ___6 ___7 ___8 ___9 ___10

Not at all *Totally*

11. Prior to your knowledge of betrayal, did you trust your husband/significant other to follow through with their commitments?

___1 ___2 ___3 ___4 ___5 ___6 ___7 ___8 ___9 ___10

Not at all *Totally*

12. Prior to your knowledge of betrayal, did you trust your husband/significant other with their recovery?

___1 ___2 ___3 ___4 ___5 ___6 ___7 ___8 ___9 ___10

Not at all *Totally*

13. After your knowledge of betrayal, do you trust your husband/significant other emotionally?

___1 ___2 ___3 ___4 ___5 ___6 ___7 ___8 ___9 ___10

Not at all *Totally*

14. After your knowledge of betrayal, do you trust your husband/significant other?

___1 ___2 ___3 ___4 ___5 ___6 ___7 ___8 ___9 ___10

Not at all *Totally*

15. After your knowledge of betrayal, do you trust your husband/significant other spiritually?

___1 ___2 ___3 ___4 ___5 ___6 ___7 ___8 ___9 ___10

Not at all *Totally*

16. After your knowledge of betrayal, do you trust your husband/significant other in social situations?

___1 ___2 ___3 ___4 ___5 ___6 ___7 ___8 ___9 ___10

Not at all *Totally*

17. After your knowledge of betrayal, do you trust your husband/significant other sexually?

___1 ___2 ___3 ___4 ___5 ___6 ___7 ___8 ___9 ___10

Not at all *Totally*

18. After your knowledge of betrayal, do you trust your husband/significant other financially?

___1 ___2 ___3 ___4 ___5 ___6 ___7 ___8 ___9 ___10

Not at all *Totally*

19. After your knowledge of betrayal, do you trust your husband/significant other parenting?

___1 ___2 ___3 ___4 ___5 ___6 ___7 ___8 ___9 ___10

Not at all *Totally*

20. After your knowledge of betrayal, do you trust your husband/significant other with general responsibilities?

___1 ___2 ___3 ___4 ___5 ___6 ___7 ___8 ___9 ___10

Not at all *Totally*

21. After your knowledge of betrayal, do you trust your husband/significant other in other extended family relationships?

___1 ___2 ___3 ___4 ___5 ___6 ___7 ___8 ___9 ___10

Not at all *Totally*

22. After your knowledge of betrayal, do you trust your husband/significant other to keep their word?

___1 ___2 ___3 ___4 ___5 ___6 ___7 ___8 ___9 ___10

Not at all *Totally*

23. After your knowledge of betrayal, do you trust your husband/significant other to follow through with their commitments?

___1 ___2 ___3 ___4 ___5 ___6 ___7 ___8 ___9 ___10

Not at all *Totally*

24. After your knowledge of betrayal, do you trust your husband/significant other with their recovery?

___1 ___2 ___3 ___4 ___5 ___6 ___7 ___8 ___9 ___10

Not at all *Totally*

As you scored trust in your relationship, which areas came up that trust is still reasonably stuck?

1.________________ 6.________________

2.________________ 7.________________

3.________________ 8.________________

4.________________ 9.________________

5.________________ 10.________________

As you scored trust in your relationship which areas were at the very bottom of the trust?

1.________________ 6.________________

2.________________ 7.________________

3.________________ 8.________________

4.________________ 9.________________

5.________________ 10.________________

As you scored trust in your relationship which areas were in the middle of trust?

1.______________________ 6.______________________

2.______________________ 7.______________________

3.______________________ 8.______________________

4.______________________ 9.______________________

5.______________________ 10.______________________

Write what you think and feel about your trust scores.

Your relationship has areas of trust that will need further work for sure. Each area will be different as far as earning and giving trust. In some cases if he is being trustworthy in an area, in time you will give him the gift of your re-trust in that area. In some areas you may have to give trust as you go or even give trust first to start the process.

You can choose which area of trust you would like to rebuild first. You can mutually agree on a plan, he can establish consequences if he doesn't follow through and you can set boundaries if doesn't do his consequences (see boundaries section).

Him becoming completely trustworthy will be a process. You'll see the areas that are weaker and that would be a good place to start. I do have to highlight separation if he is a sex addict, addict of any type, or has characteristics that make him qualify as having intimacy anorexia. If he has any of these, he's going to be emotionally immature. (watch the DVD: *When You Marry A Child Don't Expect A Man Right Away*)

If he's an addict, he'll need to do a recovery that actually fosters him maturing and moving away from "doing what he feels like doing" into "doing the right thing."

Recovery Plan

If he is in recovery he should have a plan that looks similar to what is outlined below. If he is an addict and he doesn't have a plan similar to what is below, trust will be a longer and harder road to achieve.

1. The 5 Commandment's are actions that he does daily (pray, read recovery material, calls, meetings, pray again.) It's very important he's in an all-male accountability group since, as I stated earlier, men make men.
2. Have a sponsor.
3. Working through the *101 Freedom Exercises* and *Steps to Freedom* workbook.
4. Attends therapy, if needed. If abuse or intimacy anorexia is involved this is especially important.
5. Polygraphs quarterly the first year, 6 months second year, annually until mutually-agreed upon.
6. Have a mutual check-in meeting on an agreed upon basis (weekly, biweekly, monthly). You both check in on recovery progress.

These are the basics for him beginning to become trustworthy as it relates to recovery. If he needs help with any of these, he can call our office and make an appointment to talk to a counselor. In the space below, write out some of your thoughts and feelings about him being trustworthy.

____

____

____

____

____

Trust Giving

Here is the tough part of trusting again. If he is not trustworthy, you might not feel required to re-trust him. However, if he is maturing and trying to rebuild trust you will then have to face the "giving trust" side of the equation.

Since it's totally impossible to completely earn trust, you can say if you do x,y and z then trust will be given with no questions asked. You can then be all in. He can't put a certain amount in the trust account and then you automatically give trust.

He can be totally trustworthy (and I have seen this) and you still could choose to withhold trust. You might also choose to give trust since giving trust is 100% yours to give.

You might have to confront some real concerns, feelings or existing paradigms. A paradigm is the way you currently look at or frame an idea. For example, the next two statements are paradigms:

1. He has to do everything for me to trust.
2. He can do his part then I still have to choose to trust.

Depending on the paradigm you believe in or promise you made yourself, you may have some challenges.

Let me give you some paradigms and promises as examples that can impede giving trust even when he is trustworthy.

1. He needs to make me feel safe.
2. I am responsible for how I feel and I can choose to feel safe.

---

1. I promised myself if he ever did X I would never stay married.
2. I have to consider several things now that I've actually been betrayed.

---

1. I have to control him to be safe in the future.
2. He must control himself and I must set up measures for reasonable safety.

---

1. I'll never have sex with him again.
2. I really respect how hard he is working his recovery and I desire sex and it's healthy to want sex.

I could go on and on about the paradigm that could make giving trust while in pain a challenge. Are there any paradigms you have bought into or created that are making giving trust a challenge for you? If so list them below.

1.____________________

2.____________________

3.____________________

4.____________________

5.____________________

6.____________________

7.____________________

8.____________________

9.____________________

10.____________________

Reframing these paradigms, how else could you look at them? If you need help from other women, feel free to reach out to them.

1.____________________

2.____________________

3.____________________

4.____________________

5.____________________

6.____________________

7.____________________

8.____________________

9.____________________

10.____________________

Write your thoughts about the paradigm you're working through.

____

____

____

____

____

____

____

____

____

Promises are something we make in our heart. So even if he is trustworthy the thought of "but you promised yourself you wouldn't...." comes up. In the space below, write any and all promises you made during the trauma that may have kept you alive but may now be in the way for you to give trust.

1. ______________________
2. ______________________
3. ______________________
4. ______________________
5. ______________________
6. ______________________
7. ______________________
8. ______________________
9. ______________________
10. ______________________

Promises are different, however, since you had the power to make them you have the power to break them. You will need to write a letter of thank you to each promise separately and a goodbye, divorce or breaking the promise to each promise as well. In the below space write the date you broke these promises and who you shared these letters with.

	Person	Date
1.	______________	___/___/___
2.	______________	___/___/___
3.	______________	___/___/___
4.	______________	___/___/___
5.	______________	___/___/___
6.	______________	___/___/___
7.	______________	___/___/___
8.	______________	___/___/___
9.	______________	___/___/___
10.	______________	___/___/___

I shared this with ______________

on

___/___/___

Fear

Fear is another aspect that can keep you from deciding to want to re-trust. Fear is a feeling not a fact or truth. Fear can be legitimate or illegitimate. You can acknowledge your fears and process through them. In the space below write out your fears about retrusting him.

1.______________________________

2.______________________________

3.______________________________

4.______________________________

5.______________________________

6.______________________________

7.______________________________

8.______________________________

9.______________________________

10.______________________________

I want you to talk to other women who know you and walk through each fear with them. After you process each fear separately write down what you feel or think about that fear today.

1.______________________________

2.______________________________

3.______________________________

4.______________________________

5.______________________________

6.______________________________

7.______________________________

8.______________________________

9.______________________________

10.______________________________

Trust is a really large issue for the partner of betrayal trauma. I want you to write your insights and narrative about trust, him being trustworthy and you giving trust again.

Sex is by far an area where partners of betrayal trauma are most impacted. However, like sexual abuse survivors respond in a myriad of ways to sexual abuse so do partners of betrayal trauma.

Some partners want to immediately resume sex on a frequent or regular interval. They get more creative, initiate more, and report being more sexually engaged than ever before. For others, sex is the last thing they want to talk about, do, or think about with him again. For them, they are glad this is the last chapter in the workbook.

There are those who feel hurt for a season and then move toward sex slowly but steadily back to their normal pace and style of sexuality.

In my more than thirty years of talking through this process of sexuality, engagement, and reengagement I've learned a few factors that can contribute to the process of sexual reconstruction.

Sexual abuse: If either of you have a sexual abuse history that is still a secret or not properly addressed, this will be a factor on the sexuality of any couple.

This applies to me. *Yes* ____ *No* ____

This applies to him. *Yes* ____ *No* ____

Sexual Infidelity: Sex outside of marriage is a different level of betrayal than pornography or masturbation. The other person's relationship to you (i.e., friend, neighbor, employee) can also be a betrayal if the sex between them felt relational.

This applies to me. *Yes* ____ *No* ____

Sexual Self Esteem: Every woman has a sexual esteem. Rate your sexual esteem before betrayal and after betrayal.

Before

___1 ___2 ___3 ___4 ___5 ___6 ___7 ___8 ___9 ___10

Low *High*

After

___1 ___2 ___3 ___4 ___5 ___6 ___7 ___8 ___9 ___10

Low *High*

Sexual Conversation: Each woman has a comfort level discussing sexuality, especially their own sexuality. Some women are very comfortable talking about sexuality and some are almost verbally paralyzed talking about sex. Below, rate your comfort level in discussing sexuality before the betrayal and after the betrayal.

Before

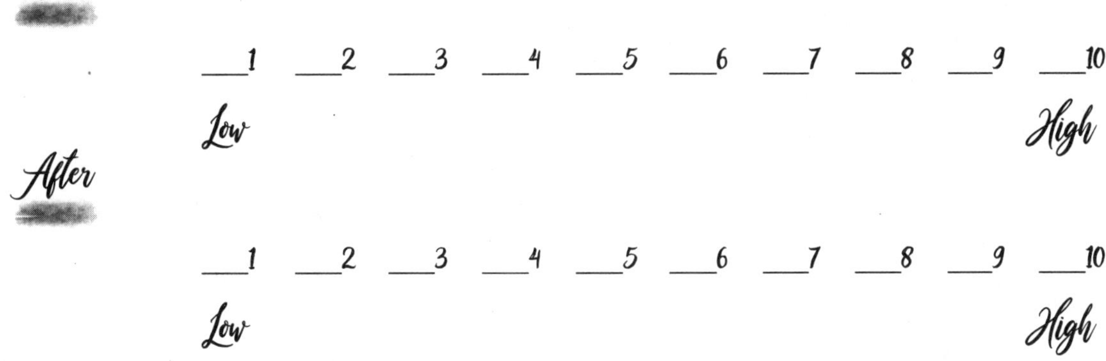

Sexual Engagement: Some women are verbally and physically engaged during the sex act. Some women are very passive and silent during sex. Below, rate your verbal and physical engagement during sex before the betrayal and after the betrayal.

Before

___1 ___2 ___3 ___4 ___5 ___6 ___7 ___8 ___9 ___10

Low *High*

After

___1 ___2 ___3 ___4 ___5 ___6 ___7 ___8 ___9 ___10

Low *High*

Sexual Initiation: Some women confidently ask for sex regularly from their husband or significant other. Some women never or almost never ask their spouse for sex verbally. Below, rate your confidence level in initiating sex before the betrayal and after the betrayal.

Before

___1 ___2 ___3 ___4 ___5 ___6 ___7 ___8 ___9 ___10

Low *High*

After

___1 ___2 ___3 ___4 ___5 ___6 ___7 ___8 ___9 ___10

Low *High*

Body Image: Some women regardless of shape or size are very confident about and like their bodies. Some women no matter the shape or size are critical and don't like their bodies. Below, rate your confidence about your body before the betrayal and after the betrayal.

Before

___1 ___2 ___3 ___4 ___5 ___6 ___7 ___8 ___9 ___10

Low *High*

After

___1 ___2 ___3 ___4 ___5 ___6 ___7 ___8 ___9 ___10

Low *High*

Body Familiarity: Some women are very familiar with their sexual body and orgasm regularly. Some women are not sexually familiar with how their sexual body works. Below, rate your familiarity with your sexual body before the betrayal and after the betrayal.

Before

___1 ___2 ___3 ___4 ___5 ___6 ___7 ___8 ___9 ___10

Low *High*

After

___1 ___2 ___3 ___4 ___5 ___6 ___7 ___8 ___9 ___10

Low *High*

Sexual Messaging: Some women grew up with the message that sex was good, great, pleasurable, and enjoy sex. Some women were raised that sex was bad, dirty and to save it only for the one you love.

My family/early messages about sex was:

___1 ___2 ___3 ___4 ___5 ___6 ___7 ___8 ___9 ___10

Poor *Healthy*

Emotional Intimacy: For some of you, your marriage was close and connected outside the bedroom. For others he or you have been emotionally distant. If the distance was extreme, visit Intimacyanorexia.com. Emotional intimacy is vital to elicit sexual desire. Below, rate you level of emotional intimacy before the betrayal and after the betrayal.

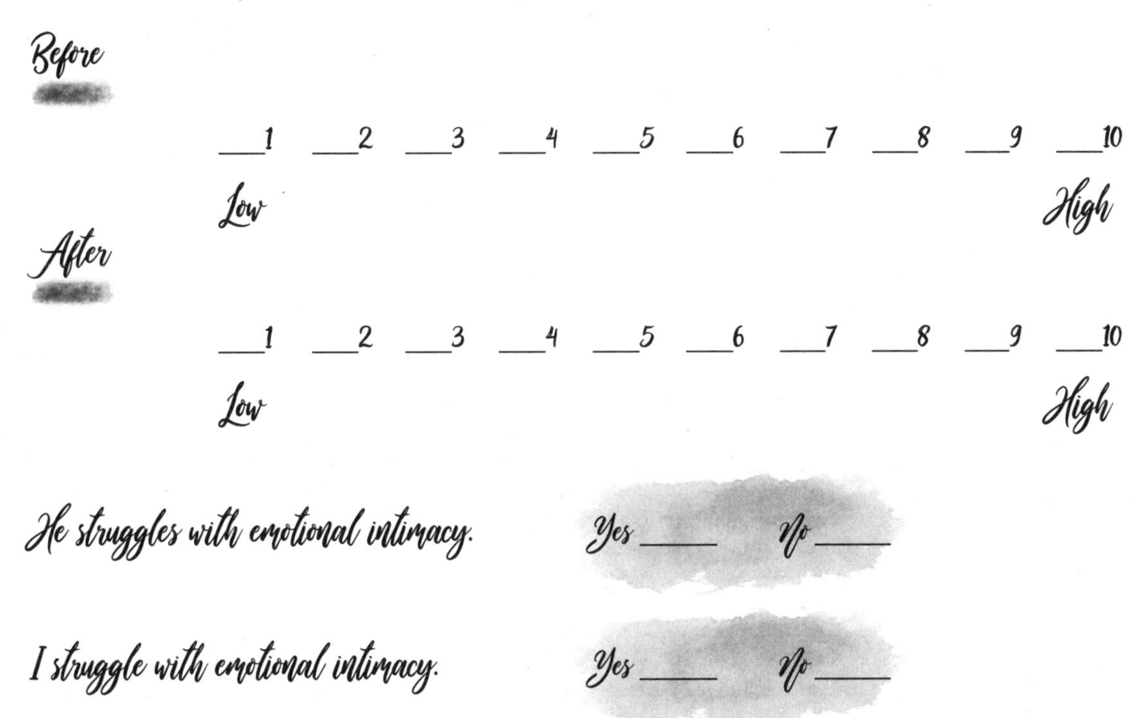

Before

___1 ___2 ___3 ___4 ___5 ___6 ___7 ___8 ___9 ___10

Low *High*

After

___1 ___2 ___3 ___4 ___5 ___6 ___7 ___8 ___9 ___10

Low *High*

He struggles with emotional intimacy. *Yes* _____ *No* _____

I struggle with emotional intimacy. *Yes* _____ *No* _____

Sex for control/reward: Some women never use sex in a controlling or rewarding manner. Some women totally use sex in a controlling or rewarding manner. Below, rate you level of control/reward before the betrayal and after the betrayal.

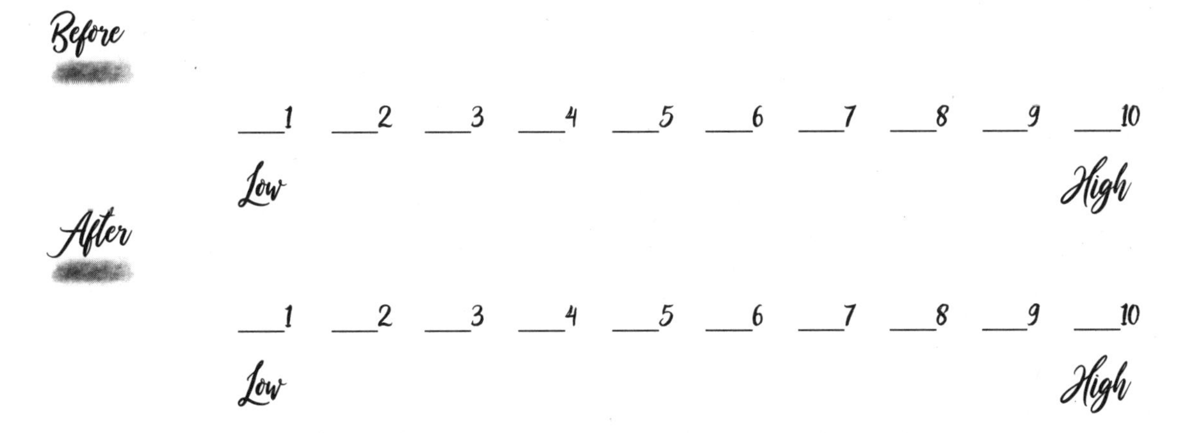

Before

___1 ___2 ___3 ___4 ___5 ___6 ___7 ___8 ___9 ___10

Low *High*

After

___1 ___2 ___3 ___4 ___5 ___6 ___7 ___8 ___9 ___10

Low *High*

As you went through these questions, write out what you are thinking and feeling about your sexuality before and after betrayal.

Now you must consider him sexually. He is a real factor in your mutual sexuality.

Does he have a sex addiction? Yes ____ No ____

If yes, is he already in recovery? Yes ____ No ____

Is he emotionally present during sex? Below, rate his level of being emotionally present during sex before the betrayal and after the betrayal (if applicable).

Before

___1 ___2 ___3 ___4 ___5 ___6 ___7 ___8 ___9 ___10

Low *High*

After

___1 ___2 ___3 ___4 ___5 ___6 ___7 ___8 ___9 ___10

Low *High*

I felt alone during and after sex with him. Yes ____ No ____

Has he been a patient/impatient lover?

___1 ___2 ___3 ___4 ___5 ___6 ___7 ___8 ___9 ___10

Impatient *Patient*

Has he been selfish sexually or giving selflessly?

_1 ___2 ___3 ___4 ___5 ___6 ___7 ___8 ___9 ___10

Selfish *Giving*

Does he make pleasing you a priority? Yes ____ No ____

Has he broken all contact with any women he betrayed you with? Yes ____ No ____

In the space below, write your thoughts or fears about who he has been and is sexually in your marriage/ relationship.

____

____

____

____

____

____

____

____

____

____

____

____

____

____

There are many factors unique to you and him that influence your sexual journey. In my book *Intimacy: 100 Day Guide to Lasting Relationships,* I list three tips for relational sex. These tips are:

1. Eyes open
2. Lights on
3. Nurturing conversation

When I discuss the topic of sex, I'm talking about connected sex not disconnected sex. The goal is to have connected sex on an agreed amount of frequency with mutual initiation. This is what a healthy sex life is.

1. Address any past issues.
2. Address any sex addiction issues.
3. Communicate your feelings about where you stand sexually at present time.
4. Work through your side of sexuality with a professional if needed.
5. Create a process to move into sexuality.

The plunge into sexuality is much like giving trust. There is a point in which his trustworthiness and your ability to extend trust sexually merge. This is a journey with many variables. Time is helpful but not the sole solution. If someone is afraid for whatever reason to jump off a twelve-foot diving board, time doesn't change the twelve feet. There is a time in sexuality where you jump.

Sexuality is risky and it doesn't guarantee safety. Sexuality is inherently risky for all of us throughout our marriage and relationship. For the partner of betrayal trauma, the courage to initiate this jump is huge, and if/when you take that plunge, applaud yourself for the courage. As you actively address issues going toward sexuality also applaud yourself.

My feelings about sexuality with him today are:

The person or team I will put together to help me walk through sexuality:

1.
2.
3.
4.

I'll know I'm actively pursuing sexuality if I:

1.
2.
3.
4.

I'll know if I'm not actively pursuing sexuality if:

1.
2.
3.
4.

In the next space, write a letter to your sexuality.

I shared my letter for my sexuality with ______________

on

____/____/____

If you have walked through this workbook, I truly applaud you.

You have looked at:

Trust	Your trauma history	The betrayal
The disclosure	Consequences	Losses
Anger	Busyness	Forgiveness

Just look behind you and see what you have traveled through. Partner betrayal is real and an important part of recovery. I hope you have also availed yourself of the *Partners Recovery Guide* and the *Beyond Love: 12 Step Guide* for Partners.

You deserve a big thank you for doing all this hard work for something you did not cause. I want you to know, I believe you are a hero in your own life. In these last pages write out a thank you letter to yourself and include your moments of insight, growth and change you have seen in your life because of all the hard work you have done throughout these pages. You are a Hero!

Thank you:

Appendix

Feelings Exercise

1. I feel (put feeling word here) when (put a present situation when you feel this).
2. I first remember feeling (put the same feeling word here) when (explain earliest occurrence of this feeling).

Rules for couples: 1- No examples about each other or the relationship. 2 - Maintain Eye Contact 3- No Feedback

Abandoned
Abused
Aching
Accepted
Accused
Accepting
Admired
Adored
Adventurous
Affectionate
Agony
Alienated
Aloof
Aggravated
Agreeable
Aggressive
Alive
Alone
Alluring
Amazed
Amused
Angry
Anguished
Annoyed
Anxious
Apart
Apathetic
Apologetic
Appreciated
Appreciative
Apprehensive
Appropriate
Approved
Argumentative
Aroused
Astonished
Assertive
Attached
Attacked
Attentive
Attractive
Aware
Awestruck
Badgered
Baited
Bashful
Battered
Beaten
Beautiful
Belligerent
Belittled
Bereaved
Betrayed
Bewildered
Blamed
Blaming
Bonded
Bored
Bothered
Brave
Breathless
Bristling
Broken-up
Bruised
Bubbly
Burdened
Burned
Callous
Calm
Capable
Captivated
Carefree
Careful
Careless
Caring
Cautious
Certain
Chased
Cheated
Cheerful
Childlike
Choked-up
Close
Cold
Comfortable
Comforted
Competent
Competitive
Complacent
Complete
Confident
Confused
Considerate
Consumed
Content
Cool
Courageous
Courteous
Coy
Crabby
Cranky
Crazy
Creative
Critical
Criticized
Cross
Crushed
Cuddly
Curious
Cut
Damned
Dangerous
Daring
Dead
Deceived
Deceptive
Defensive
Delicate
Delighted
Demeaned
Demoralized
Dependent
Depressed
Deprived
Deserted
Desirable
Desired
Despair
Despondent
Destroyed
Different
Dirty
Disenchanted
Disgusted
Disinterested
Dispirited
Distressed
Distrustful
Distrusted
Disturbed
Dominated
Domineering
Doomed
Doubtful
Dreadful
Eager
Ecstatic
Edgy
Edified
Elated
Embarrassed
Empowered
Empty
Enraged
Enraptured
Enthusiastic
Enticed
Esteemed
Exasperated
Excited
Exhilarated
Exposed
Fake
Fascinated
Feisty
Ferocious
Foolish
Forced
Forceful
Forgiven
Forgotten
Free
Friendly
Frightened
Frustrated
Full
Funny
Furious
Gay
Generous
Gentle
Genuine
Giddy
Giving
Goofy
Grateful
Greedy
Grief
Grim
Grimy
Grouchy
Grumpy
Hard
Harried
Hassled
Healthy
Helpful
Helpless
Hesitant
High
Hollow
Honest
Hopeful
Hopeless
Horrified
Hostile
Humiliated
Hurried
Hurt
Hyper
Ignorant
Ignored
Immature
Impatient
Important
Impotent
Impressed
Incompetent
Incomplete
Independent
Insecure
Innocent
Insignificant
Insincere
Isolated
Inspired
Insulted
Interested
Intimate
Intolerant

Involved
Irate
Irrational
Irked
Irresponsible
Irritable
Irritated
Isolated
Jealous
Jittery
Joyous
Lively
Lonely
Loose
Lost
Loving
Low
Lucky
Lustful
Mad
Maudlin
Malicious
Mean
Miserable
Misunderstood
Moody
Morose
Mournful
Mystified
Nasty
Nervous
Nice
Numb
Nurtured
Nuts
Obsessed
Offended
Open
Ornery
Out of control
Overcome
Overjoyed
Overpowered
Overwhelmed
Pampered
Panicked
Paralyzed
Paranoid
Patient
Peaceful
Pensive
Perceptive
Perturbed
Phony
Pleasant
Pleased
Positive
Powerless
Present
Precious
Pressured
Pretty
Proud
Pulled apart
Put down
Puzzled
Quarrelsome
Queer
Quiet
Raped
Ravished
Ravishing
Real
Refreshed
Regretful
Rejected
Rejuvenated
Rejecting
Relaxed
Relieved
Remarkable
Remembered
Removed
Repulsed
Repulsive
Resentful
Resistant
Responsible
Responsive
Repressed
Respected
Restless
Revolved
Riled
Rotten
Ruined
Sad
Safe
Satiated
Satisfied
Scared
Scolded
Scorned
Scrutinized
Secure
Seduced
Seductive
Self-centered
Self-conscious
Selfish
Separated
Sensuous
Sexy
Shattered
Shocked
Shot down
Shy
Sickened
Silly
Sincere
Sinking
Smart
Smothered
Smug
Sneaky
Snowed
Soft
Solid
Solitary
Sorry
Spacey
Special
Spiteful
Spontaneous
Squelched
Starved
Stiff
Stimulated
Stifled
Strangled
Strong
Stubborn
Stuck
Stunned
Stupid
Subdued
Submissive
Successful
Suffocated
Sure
Sweet
Sympathy
Tainted
Tearful
Tender
Tense
Terrific
Terrified
Thrilled
Ticked
Tickled
Tight
Timid
Tired
Tolerant
Tormented
Torn
Tortured
Touched
Trapped
Tremendous
Tricked
Trusted
Trustful
Trusting
Ugly
Unacceptable
Unapproach-
able
Unaware
Uncertain
Uncomfortable
Under control
Understanding
Understood
Undesirable
Unfriendly
Ungrateful
Unified
Unhappy
Unimpressed
Unsafe
Unstable
Upset
Uptight
Used
Useful
Useless
Unworthy
Validated
Valuable
Valued
Victorious
Violated
Violent
Voluptuous
Vulnerable
Warm
Wary
Weak
Whipped
Whole
Wicked
Wild
Willing
Wiped out
Wishful
Withdrawn
Wonderful
Worried
Worthy
Wounded
Young
Zapped

Partner Betrayal Trauma is real. Your pain and experience of betrayal has impacted all of your being and all of your relationships.

The book, workbook and step guide were designed to help guide you thoughtfully through your own personal healing from the affects of being betrayed by your spouse or significant other. The pain and trauma of being betrayed, especially sexual betrayal, by a spouse or significant other is multidimensional and multifaceted. Your pain and trauma are real and these resources will help you in your journey of recovery from this betrayal and trauma.

Book: $14.95 Workbook: $39.95 Step Guide: $14.95

WOMEN'S RECOVERY

This book offers the readers hope, along with a plan for recovery. Any woman who is a partner of a sex addict will find this book a necessity for her journey toward healing. $14.95

This is like therapy in a box for women who want to walk through the residual effects of being in a relationship with a sex addict. $39.95

This is an interactive workbook that allows the partners of sex addicts to gain insight and strength through working the Twelve Steps. $14.95

This addresses the pain, trauma, and betrayal women experience because of their partner's sex addiction, betrayal, and/or intimacy anorexia. $29.95

This DVD provides a clear path to processing your desire for safety and creates a roadmap to reclaim safety regardless of your partner or spouse's choices. $29.95

This DVD is for every woman who has experienced the pain of their partner's sex addiction or intimacy anorexia and feels stuck, confused, frustrated and unable to move on.$29.00

This DVD set helps women accept this immature reality and gives them practical ways to navigate their husband's re-maturing process if he chooses recovery. $49.99

Your pain and betrayal are real and are addressed in this DVD series. You deserve the best answer to your questions and in just under 2 hours you can have them answered for you. $69.95

In this DVD set Dr. Weiss will expose the viewer to specific reasons as to why men lie and helpful strategies to end the lying. $44.95

MEN'S RECOVERY

This book gives more current information than many professional counselors have today on sexual addiction. $22.95

This workbook will outline the best techniques to help obtain freedom from sexual addiction. $39.95

This step book is specifically written for the person desiring recovery from sexual addiction. $14.95

Offers practical tools for hearing her pain, navigating her grief and losses, discovering her expectations of you and the boundaries she may need to heal. $69.95

In this DVD you are intelligently guided through the journey you will experience if addiction is part of your marriage story. $29.95

Helps identify key points about the whys of infidelity, the types of cheaters, and how to start walking toward a healthy marriage. $49.95

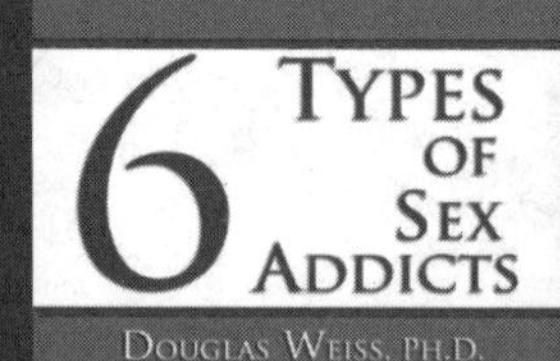

This CD will give you more information than most therapists have on sexual addiction. You will be able to finally know how you became a sexual addict and identify why you might still be relapsing. $29.95

Once you know the type of sex addict you are, Dr. Doug outlines the same treatment plan you would receive in an individual session. $29.95

This amazing DVD has 8 addicts telling their stories through directed questions. These individuals address key issues along with their journey through recovery. $19.95

INTIMACY ANOREXIA

This hidden addiction is destroying so many marriages today. In your hands is the first antidote for a person or spouse with anorexia to turn the pages on this addiction process. $22.95

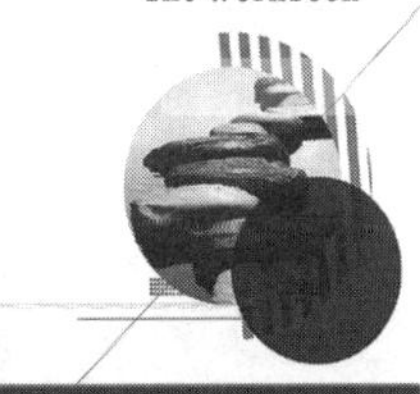

This is like therapy in a box. Inside is 100 exercises that have already been proven helpful in treating intimacy anorexia. $39.95

This is the only twelve step workbook just for intimacy anorexia. Each step gives you progress in your healing from intimacy anorexia. $14.95

This book will not only unlock the understanding of intimacy anorexia but you will also hear experiences of spouses who have found themselves married and alone. $14.95

This is the first workbook to offer practical suggestions and techniques to better navigate through recovery from your spouse's Intimacy Anorexia. $39.95

These Steps can further your healing and recovery from your spouse's Intimacy Anorexia. $14.95

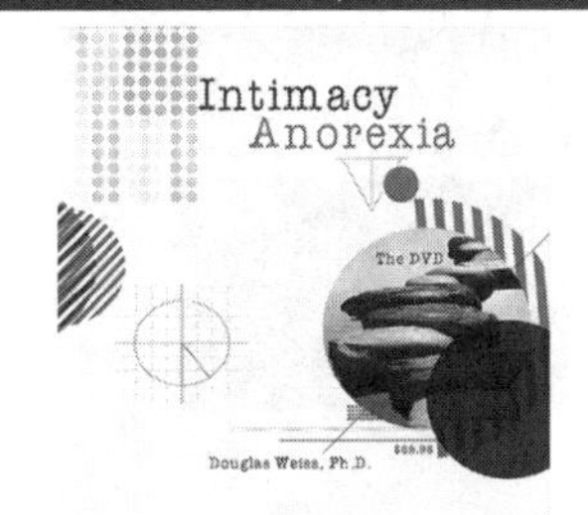

This DVD will give you the characteristics, causes and strategies of intimacy anorexia. This DVD also provides solutions for the intimacy anorexic to start their road to recovery. $69.95

This DVD is for the spouse of an intimacy/sexual anorexic. Dr. Weiss will help you to start a journey of recovery from living with a spouse with intimacy anorexia. $49.95

Dr. Weiss has put together the eight reasons why couples might be sexless and married as well as solutions for each reason for sexlessness. $49.95

MARRIAGE

Lover Spouse helps you understand marriage from a Christ-centered perspective. Christian Marriages were designed to be different, passionate, fulfilling, and long-lasting. $13.95

Upgrade Your Sex Life actually teaches you own unique sexual expression that you and your partner are pre-wired to enjoy. $16.95

In these pages you will walk with God as He creates the man, the woman and his masterpiece called marriage. $16.95

This is an eight week marriage training that actually gives you the skills to have a healthy more vibrant marriage. $59.95

This 100 Day guide can transform couples from any level of intimacy to a lifestyle of satiation with their spouse. $11.99

Dr. Weiss walks you through the creation and maintenance of your marriage. $12.95

By taking ten minutes a day to focus on each other, you can enhance your marriage in ways you'll appreciate for a lifetime. $14.99

This book helps develop faithfulness, patience, forgiveness, service, respect, kindness, and celebration, all of which contribute to an exciting, loving and wonderful relationship. $13.99

In this 12 part DVD series, you will be exposed to tried and true principles to help you learn how to really love a woman. $69.00

OTHER RESOURCES

"Born for War" teaches practical tools to defeat these sexual landmines and offers scriptural truths that empower young men to desire successfulness in the war thrust upon them. $29.95

This 2 hour DVD helps single women ages 15-30, to successfully navigate through the season of dating. $29.95

This 2 Disc DVD Series is definitely nothing you have heard before. Dr. Weiss charts new territory as to the why for sexual purity. $29.95

A gift for your daugher as she enters college. Letters to my Daughter includes my daily letters to my daughter during her first year of college. $14.95

This Worthy Series is designed for anyone who has struggled with doubting their amazing worth. DVD Set $29.95
Workbook $29.95

Within these pages of this book you will find a tried and true path for recovery from any addiction. Here you will get a biblical understanding to break the strongholds in your life forever. $22.95

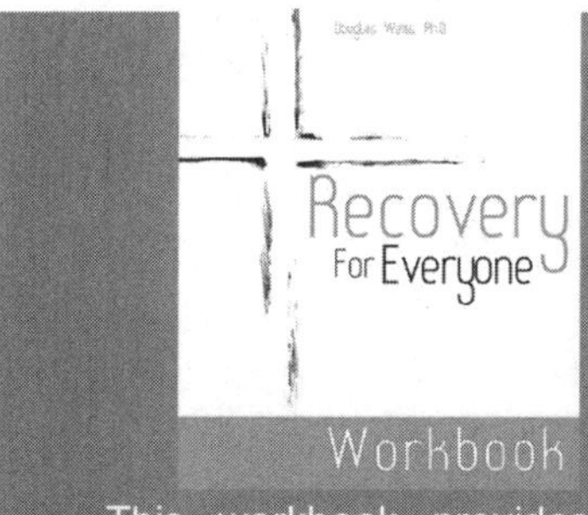

This workbook provides tips, biblical principles, techniques, and assignments that Dr. Weiss has given his addicted clients with any addiction for over twenty-five years. $39.95

These steps were derived from a Christian perspective and offer much needed insight and practical wisdom to help you get free and stay free from any addiction. $14.95

This Dvd series includes leadership training and fifty segments that are about 10 minutes in length. Churches of any size can begin a Recovery for Everyone group in their local church. $99.00

CLEAN RESOURCES

Every Christian man is born into a sexual war. The enemy attacks the young, hoping to scar them permanently and leave them ruined. But your past is not enough to keep you from the enduringly clean life you want and deserve. $16.99

This journal is designed to be used in conjunction with the Clean book and the Clean DVD set. This set can be used individually or in a church small group or accountability group. $14.99

This DVD set exposes you to many tried and true spiritual truths with very practical applications. You and your church are about to take an amazing journey towards God's insights for your freedom. $29.99

LUST FREE RESOURCES

Every man can fight for and obtain a lust free lifestyle. Once you know how to stop lust, you will realize how weak lust really can be. God gave you the power to protect those you love from the ravages of lust for the rest of your life! It's time to take it back! $13.95

This DVD series walks you through how every man can fight for and obtain a lust free lifestyle. Once you know how to stop lust, you will realize how weak lust really can be. God gave you the power to protect those you love from the ravages of lust for the rest of your life! It's time to take it back! $23.95

FREE APP!

Download Now!

NEW RELEASES

Men Make Men

Dr. Weiss takes the listeners by the hand and step-by-step walks through the creative process God used to make every man into a man of God. This practical teaching on DVD combined with the Men Make Guidebook can revitalize the men in any home or local church. DVD - $29.95 GUIDE BOOK - $11.95

Worthy

This Series is designed for anyone who has struggled with doubting their amazing worth. This insightful and pragmatic journey to worthy is one every believer should experience. You are worth this journey to see what others see - your worth! $29.95

Worthy Exercise & Step book {all in one}

This workbook has been a labor of love. I have seen countless people move from a lifestyle of worthlessness to worthy, and their lives have inspired me to write this. What you have here is a path that anyone can take to get and stay worthy. Follow this path, and you too will make the journey from worthless to worthy, just as others have. $29.95

COUNSELING

"Without the intensive, my marriage would have ended and I would not have known why. Now I am happier than ever and my marriage is bonded permanently."

Counseling Sessions

Couples are helped through critical phases of disclosure moving into the process of recovery, and rebuilding trust in relationships. We have helped many couples rebuild their relationship and grasp and implement the necessary skills for an intimate relationship.

Individual counseling offers a personal treatment plan for successful healing in your life. In just one session a counselor can help you understand how you became stuck and how to move toward freedom.

Partners of sex addicts need an advocate. Feelings of fear, hurt, anger, betrayal, and grief require a compassionate, effective response. We provide that expert guidance and direction. We have helped many partners heal through sessions that get them answers to their many questions including: "How can I trust him again?"

A counseling session today can begin your personal journey toward healing.

3 and 5 Day Intensives

in Colorado Springs, Colorado are available for the following issues:

- Partner Betrayal Trauma
- Sexual Addiction
- Marriage
- Pastors
- Partners of Sexual Addicts
- Intimacy Anorexia
- Victims of Sexual Abuse
- Adult Children of Sex Addicts
- Teenage Children of Sex Addicts
- Teens

Attendees of Intensives will receive:

- Personal attention from counselors who specialize in your area of need
- An understanding of how the addiction /anorexia and its consequences came into being
- Three counseling sessions daily
- Daily assignments to increase the productiveness of these daily sessions
- Individuals get effective counseling to recover from the effects of sexual addiction, abuse and intimacy anorexia.
- Addiction, abuse, anorexia issues are thoroughly addressed for couples and individuals. This includes the effects on the partner or family members of the addict, and how to rebuild intimacy toward a stronger relationship.

CONFERENCES

What an incredible way to deliver such a sensitive, "hush hush" topic!! Thank you from the bottom of my heart. I really enjoyed tonight's conference. Today will count as the first day of my sexual sobriety.

CLEAN is a powerful men's conference equipping men to join the battle to maintain sexual purity. In this conference, men will be given tools and biblical principles so they can get started immediately.

PURITY Mixed audiences can be impacted by *Successfully Single*, as well as *Born for War* for Male Teens and *Princes take Longer than Frogs* for Female Teens to help motivate them to fight for their sexual purity.

MEN The *Lust Free Living* or *Sex, Men & God* conferences is where men experience great personal growth and understanding into their sexuality and how to be lust free...where other speakers rarely go. *How to Really Love a Woman* is really practical training for the men in your church.

COUPLES attending the *Servant Marriage, Intimacy, 10 Minute Marriage* or *The 7 Love Agreements* Conference discover how to discuss their desires, learn the importance of marital dating, how to connect emotionally, how to let go of your past and much more.

WOMEN *How to Really Love a Man* and *Best Sex for Women* are great inspiring and practical teachings for the women in your church.

For additional conference information, including available dates, please call our office at 719-278-3708, visit our website at www.drdougweiss.org or you may also email us at lisa@drdougweiss.com